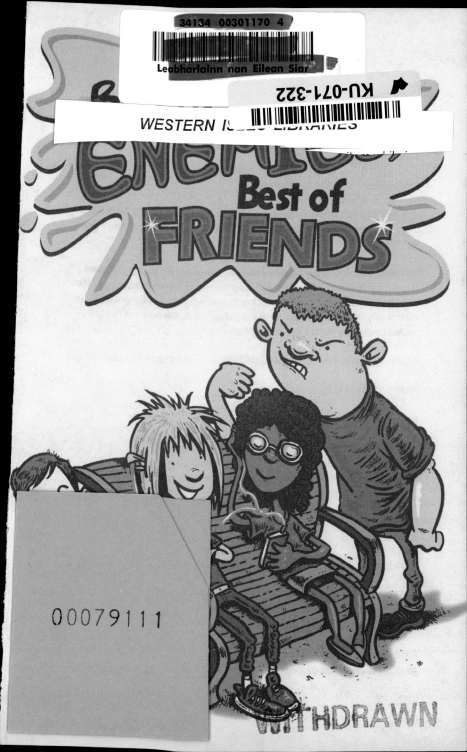

ENEMIES Best of FRIENDS

For Katie Woolley and Rasha Elsaeed, my editors.
(Editors do a great job to make books look good and should always have
at least one book dedicated to them!)

This selection copyright © Brian Moses 2011
Book copyright © Wayland 2011

First published in 2011 by Wayland

The right of Brian Moses to be identified as the compiler of this Work has
been asserted by him in accordance with the Copyright, Designs and Patents
Act, 1988.

A catalogue record for this book is available from the British Library.

ISBN: 978 0 7502 6569 0

Printed and bound by CPI Bookmarque Ltd, Croydon, CR0 4TD

The paper and board used in this paperback by Wayland
are natural recyclable products made from wood grown
in sustainable forests. The manufacturing processes conform
to the environmental regulations of the country of origin.

Wayland
338 Euston Road
London
NW1 3BH

Wayland is a division of Hachette Children's Books,
an Hachette UK company,
www.hachette.co.uk

*For more information about the poets included in this book,
go to www.waylandbooks.co.uk.*

Words From Brian Moses...

There was a bully in my school when I was young and there were three ways of dealing with him. The first was to run and keep running. The second was to turn and fight him. The third was to join his gang.

Joining his gang didn't mean that he be friends with you. He didn't understand any kind of relationship where he wasn't in complete control. It just meant that he'd leave you alone, providing you did what he asked of you.

Fortunately I had friends, real friends, friends who stuck up for me when the bully was after me. That's the value of true friendship. I felt sorry for the bully, sorry he'd never know how good it is to have friends who want you as a friend.

When I was compiling this book I wondered how to arrange the poems. I eventually decided to start with the negative and move to the positive. I wanted the sequence of poems to show that life can, and will, get better if you are bullied...

The centre section of the book looks at the complications of friendship. Sometimes you do have to work at it, to learn to forgive, and to overlook things that annoy you at times.

The final section emphasises the positive aspects of friendship, the great feelings you get when you find those friends who value you as much as you value them.

We do need everybody sitting on the friendship bench (see the poem on page 78), and given time it may eventually happen.

Brian Moses

Best Of Friends

You Are The Chosen One

Today
we are giving you
our special surprise.

Yes, you.
You have been chosen.

Today
and tomorrow
and next week
and

until we decide
to choose
someone else.

Because we can.

Mike Jubb

Best Of Enemies

Sprat Elliot

Sprat Elliot,
a whale of a boy,
was our school bully.
"Cheats never prosper…"
"Bullies never win…"
we would shout from ten miles away.
But Sprat always did.
Even from ten miles.

Peter Dixon

"The most I can do for my friend
is simply be his friend."
Henry David Thoreau

How To Invent 'Them'

All these words:
Them, Those, They
need capital Ts.

Close your eyes
and picture Them
with sticks or knives,

imagine Them
coming toward you
with hate in Their eyes.

Forget They have dreams,
sing songs, play games,
forget They have grandmothers

and individual names,
forget They get hiccups
or bite Their nails. Instead

see all Their ways as strange:
Their food, Their clothes,
the way They talk. Criticise

how They look, give Them
nick-names, share jokes
about Them with friends.

Tell yourself – whatever you have
They will take. When bad things happen
They are to blame.

For this to work, remember
– divide everyone
into Us or Them.

Mandy Coe

"Fear makes strangers of people
who would be friends."
Shirley MacLaine

When Billy Came Back...

Nobody felt safe anymore,
the bully was out to settle old scores.
Everyone vanished behind closed doors...

When Billy came back...

He was solid, built like a lumberjack,
It was permanent alert, he was out to attack,
no colours anymore, everything looked black...

When Billy came back...

And Billy wasn't happy till he'd made someone cry,
he'd twist your ear and jab at your eye,
then sneeringly say, "You're about to die."

When Billy came back...

Like a heat seeking missile, he'd home in on you,
a volcanic explosion as his anger grew,
you'd be begging for mercy by the time he was through...

When Billy came back...

And everyone else would be urging him on
saying, "Go on Billy, give him one for me."
For when Billy was beating up somebody else,
then Billy was leaving you be.

When Billy came back...

And it wasn't just bottles, it was bones he smashed...

When Billy came back,
when Billy came back,
when Billy came back...

   Brian Moses

And How Was School Today?

Each day they ask: And how was school today?
Behind my mask, I shrug and say OK.

Upstairs, alone, I blink away the tears
Hearing again their scornful jeers and sneers.

Hearing again them call me by those names
As they refused to let me join their games.

Feeling again them mock me with their glares
As they pushed past me rushing down the stairs.

What have I done? Why won't they let me in?
Why do they snigger? What's behind that grin?

Each day they ask: And how was school today?
Behind my mask, I shrug and say OK.

John Foster

Cyber Bully

She said she was my Facebook friend
She said I was her mate
She poked me and she joked with me
She told me I was great

Then she took my picture on her phone
And put it on the net
I told her Stop! She said she hadn't
Even started yet

She sent me texts and emails
She said I smelt of poo
She disrespects me every day
I don't know what to do

Somehow she stole my password
Now my life is not my own
I'm virtually cut adrift
And feeling all alone

My life has caught a virus
That infects me every day
Tell me how can I unfriend her?
There must surely be a way

Roger Stevens

Grrl Power

Make sure that wen u c me nxt u drop ur things n run
it's tym 2 knock u dwn a peg — it's tym 2 ave sum fun.
I'll shred ur stupid lttle bag n tear ur pretty dress
n wen I'm finished princess grrl, ule b an awful mess.

O yeh? Ur tuff? Well bring it on, can't w8 2 c u try.
Toe 2 toe we grrls will go — who'll b the 1st 2 cry?
I've w8ed 4 this moment since we started out @ skool
uve always thort ur number 1 — so tuff, so brave, so cool.

O wow! Big grrl! Uve got the mouth but ave u got the guts
to slug it out with hnds n feet, get bruises, grazes, cuts?
The winning grrl (that's me 4 sure) becomes the Y6 queen,
let's meet @ 8, enuff debate — I'm ready 2 get mean.

No problems, hun, 8's fyn with me — im burstin' 4 this fyt,
the sight ov u all blck n blu will really make my nite.
I'll stand above u arms held up — the winnr wiv my prize:
knowin' that I've knocked u out n cut u down 2 size.

Matt Goodfellow

Who's There?

I'm hunched
in the dark,

crouched
like a question mark.

The computer glows
as their words
stab the screen.

Inside,
a scream grows,

as their taunts
haunt my space.

The words blur,
as I blink back
tears.

All of my fears
stalk
the screen

as their barbs
punctuate cyber space.

Anonymous,
they hide their faces
behind their jibes.

Alone,
in my home,
no longer safe

as their words
become sticks
and stones;

they own
the book
of spite.   *Pie Corbett*

Whose Army?

Every day at half past three
Barry Goldsmith and his mates
Hang around the school gates
Usually they let me be

Last night they picked on Rupert Sloane
Barry Goldsmith and his mates
Rupert Sloane was leaving late
Said they'd escort Rupert home

I said No! You leave him be.
You and whose army? Barry said.
Leave him be – or you are dead!
But I was one and they were three.

The bullies marched Rupert away
I wandered lonely through the town
Thinking how I'd let him down
And Rupert's not in school today

Roger Stevens

Bullies And Their Friends

Bullies have gangs and never walk alone.
They never speak to you one to one,
it's always some little friend who says,
"Watch it, you're dead! My big mate's going to get
   you, right!"

Bullies' friends are always small.
By themselves they're nothing, nobodies
but when they're with their big mates
they think they're big hard tough-guy fighters.

Bullies and their friends are always small people inside,
pretending that they're really tough
when really they're frightened nobodies, scared to be
   alone.

If you do catch them alone
they will be just as scared as you might be
and just as likely to walk away silently
as they are to start a fight
because bullies and their friends are cowards.
Bullies and their friends are cowards.

Paul Cookson

New Boy

He stood alone in the playground
Scuffed his shoes and stared at the ground
He'd come half way through term from the Catholic school
On the other side of town.

He'd a brand new blazer and cap on
Polished shoes and neatly cut hair
Blew on his fists, looked up and half-smiled
Pretending he didn't care.

And I remembered when I'd been new
And no one had spoken to me
I'd almost cried as I stood alone
Hiding my misery.

Heart said I should go over,
Share a joke or play the fool
But I was scared of looking stupid
In front of the rest of the school.

At break someone said they'd seen him
Crying in the geography test
And when he came out they pointed and laughed
And I laughed along with the rest.

In my dreams I'd always stood alone
Believing I was the best
But in the cold playground of everyday life
I was no better than the rest.

Gareth Owen

"It takes a great deal of bravery
to stand up to your enemies,
just as much to stand up to your friends."
Albus Dumbledore from *Harry Potter
and the Philosopher's Stone* by J. K. Rowling

The Bully

The bully was always waiting
down the lane by the big tree
or further along at the churchyard gate.

He was someone to steer clear of,
something to avoid, if you could,
like a bad smell from a blocked drain.

He was dangerous,
like a piranha.
One scowl could strip you to the bone.

Most times he wanted sweets,
some days money.
Money made him smile,
money meant you were all right,
safe, for a while.

Once he twisted my arm
so far behind my back
I thought it would snap.

I closed my eyes and screamed inside.
If you let him know it hurt you
he'd do it all the more.

That was when I had no money to give
and I'd eaten my sweets,
but he must have smelt the chocolate
on my breath.

Then the postman came by
and heard the commotion.

"All right lad," he said.
"Let him go."
"That lad's bad," he said.
I didn't need telling that.

The next time no one saved me.
I shouted and waved my free arm
but it HURT, it hurt like mad,
all day and all the next day too.
There had to be something I could do.
Dad would have said
"Fight your own battles."
Mum was too busy to notice:
"I broke an arm today Mum."
"Oh lovely," she'd say absent-mindedly,
"You must have worked hard."

Robin Hood wouldn't have stood for it.
He'd have rounded up Little John
and Will Scarlet and let the bully have it.

So I talked to Katie,
Katie who helped out on dangerous missions
for a packet of salt and vinegar
or a bag of potato sticks.

She said she could fix him.
It would cost of course,
these things always did.
Hit women come expensive.

When he caught me that night
on the road home,
I knew he'd got it coming.
I almost told him.

Next morning Katie tipped him up
in the mud at the side of the road.
She, and the flying squad she controlled,
ran to school with his trousers.

In the playground, we wound down
the Union Jack that flapped
at the top of our flag pole,
then tied his trousers to the wire
and raised them as high as we could.

When the bully appeared he was crying,
he was actually crying,
and for one brief awful moment
I almost felt sorry for him.

We wound down his trousers
and handed them back.
He didn't say anything,
just wiped his face
with the flat of his hand
and took them away.

Later that day he found me
in a spot just short of home.
He stood at some distance
and scowled. "I'll get you,"
he spat. "I'll make you pay,
if it takes all year,
if it takes.................."

"And we'll get you too,"
I blurted out.
"We'll pay you back
in a different way."

He spat again,
just missing my feet,
then turned and stomped off
down our street.

Brian Moses

"You can always tell a real friend: when
you've made a fool of yourself he doesn't
feel you've done a permanent job."
Lawrence J. Peter

The Bully

I'm in the playground, alone, miserable,
And why? 'Cause' I'm the bully, that everybody fears.
They don't know the true me, I'm just like them,
But they don't think so,
They think I'm big, tough, mean, scary and fierce,
With a desire to hurt and pick on people,
That's only one side of me,
The side when I get irritated and antagonised.
All I want is a friend,
Someone to cheer me up when I am depressed,
Someone to calm me down when I am fuming.
I kick stones, hands in my pockets, head down,
no smile on my face.
I act tough, just to get a gang of friends,
But it never works.
I'm in the playground, alone, miserable,
And why? 'Cause' I'm the bully that everbody fears

Megan Jones (age 10)

Barry

The teachers saw
a big, round, open, honest face.
A laughing, happy, jolly boy.
They noticed he was clumsy,
but good-natured
and always ready to help.

So popular.
Just one look was enough
for an *experienced* eye
to be completely taken in.
Barry was an artist
in the craft of bullying.

"Oh, Miss, I *am* sorry.
I tripped and spilt my water
all over Michael's painting
and he'd been working
so hard on it
for Parents' Evening."

To me (but for her benefit):
"I'll help you
clear it up.
I am *so* sorry."
The painting, not quite ruined,
is swiftly obliterated by

his eager attempts
with paper towels
to make amends.

In the playground, after Art,
the broad grin and
the hand clamped on the shoulder
say to the whole world
(any teachers watching?)
We're good mates:

no – *Best Friends*.
No one that matters ever hears
(as fingers grip and twist
the pinchful of flesh
on the neck, behind the ear)
the yelp

covered by him
bawling out a joke
at the top of his voice.
Only the ice-bright glint
behind the eyes is real,
the needle stare:

"You forgot my
little present
this morning.
I waited by the gate,
but you were late.
You're getting careless.

Accidents happen to
people who break their promises.
So don't forget tomorrow
                                   – right?"

Mick Gowar

Wish List For The Bully In Your Life

I wish you nasty illnesses
Like mumps and chicken pox
I wish you nice surprises
Like scorpions hiding in your socks

I hope that you get locked inside
The snake cage at the zoo
I hope your dog has diarrhoea
In your favourite shoe

I'd like to think of you dressed in
A tutu pink and bright
While playing for the rugby team
With fairy wings so white

May all your teeth fall out at once
May headlice love your hair
May wasps infest your underpants
Sting everything in there

May your nose be always running
May you suffer from B.O.
May flies and skunks surround you
Wherever you may go

I wish you crusty pimples
And bad breath every day
I wish – I wish – I wish – I wish
I wish you'd go away!

Paul Cookson

"If you haven't learned the meaning
of friendship, you really haven't
learned anything."
Muhammad Ali

The Fight

There's a fight on the playground today –
  Two big boys from Mr Magee's
Are knocking the daylights out of each other
  Under the trees.

The girls are silent and staring
  And Clare whispers "Stop it Paul"
As the fighting gets wilder and feet jab out
  And fingers maul.

I watch, and I'm glad it's not Joe
  And me in that horrible space –
Not my stomach winded, not my nose bleeding,
  Not my burning face.

The sky is bright. Two planes fly
  Out from the base, while one
Boy holds the other down with his knee
  And breathes "You done?"

There's a fight on the playground today –
  Paul Topple from Mr Magee's
Is knocking the daylights out of John Randall
  Under the trees.

Fred Sedgwick

Dobbo's First Swimming Lesson

Dobbo's fists
spiked me to the playground wall
nailed me to the railings.

The plastic ball
he kicked against my skinny legs
on winter playtimes

Bounced a stinging red-hot bruise
across the icy tarmac.

The day we started swimming
we all jumped in
laughed and splashed, sank beneath
the funny tasting water.

Shivering in a corner
Dobbo crouched, stuck to the side
sobbing like my baby brother
when all the lights go out.

David Harmer

Tell

It started a week after my first day.
To begin with he was friendly, charming.
All smiles.

Let me sit near him in class.
Helped with my work.
Made me feel safe. Welcome.

Then. Wham!
Everything changed.
He got nasty.

Put me down. Said I'd never
amount to anything.
I was thick. Stupid.

Got people to laugh at me.
Made me look an idiot
in front of the class.

Look at the new boy crying.

I know what you're thinking.
Tell someone, right?
To beat a bully, you have to tell.

Answer me this, then:
Who do I tell when the bully is
my teacher?

Matt Goodfellow

"There is nothing on this earth more
to be prized than true friendship."
Saint Thomas Aquinas

Unspoken

He's always had a fear of heights.

Climbing halfway up the wall-bars
Is as much as he can cope.

He clings, white-knuckled.
He longs for Gym to end
So he can spend
The playtime break, recovering.

The others are back down again
And sit, as ordered, at the PE teacher's feet.

The teacher purposely leans
Against the bottom rungs
Then, rhythmically, with his body,
Rocks the wall-bars
Back and forth.

Back and forth.

Back and forth.

The boy clings, crablike,
His arms and legs entwined
About the wooden bars –
Praying he will not fall;
Praying it will all soon end.

But the PE teacher is in no hurry.

For this is the session
He most enjoys.

Trevor Harvey

"Do not protect yourself by a fence,
but rather by your friends."
Czechoslovakian Proverb

Enemies Or Friends?

Jaynie No Mates

My pal Marty
Thinks he's smart, but he
Is a few peanuts short of a party.

My pal Roxette
Thinks she's clever, yet
She's a few DVDs short of a box set.

My pal Dixon
He's very thick, some
Say he's a Homer short of the Simpsons.

My pal Charlotte
In her brain there's not a lot
She's a few lightbulbs short of a megawatt.

My pal Sanjit
He's a nitwit
He's several sausage rolls short of a picnic.

My name's Jayne
And to my shame
I had a party and nobody came.
Was it something I said?   *Kate Snow*

I Wish I Was A Robot

When robots are fighting
they don't feel pain.
They bash one another
again and again.

They clang when they crash.
They rattle and crunch.
Have head-on collisions
and don't stop for lunch.

I wish I was like them
then I'd suffer no pain
when punched and kicked
and punched again.

If I was a robot
I could cope with a lot.
If I was a robot.
But, sadly, I'm not.

Bernard Young

Remember Me?

Remember me?
I am the boy who sought friendship;
The boy you turned away.
I the boy who asked you
If I too might play.
I the face at the window
When your party was inside.
I the lonely figure
Who walked away and cried.
I the one who hung around,
A punchbag for your games.
Someone you could kick and beat,
Someone to call names.
But how strange is the change
After time has hurried by,
Four years have passed since then,
Now I'm not so quick to cry.
I'm bigger and I'm stronger,
I've grown a foot in height.
Suddenly I'M popular
And YOU'RE left out the light.
I could, if I wanted,
Be so unkind to you.

I would only have to say
And the other boys would do.
But the memory of my pain
Holds back the revenge I'd planned
And instead, I feel much stronger
By offering you my hand.

Ray Mather

"The best way to destroy an enemy
is to make him a friend."
Abraham Lincoln

Dear Michael,

Do you remember when we used to laugh together and make each other smile so easily?

Did you forget how we used to run around the playground together, Making squeaky noises, and how everyone told us we were insane?

Have you kept in your mind how we annoyed everyone in the theatre as we mocked the screen and threw popcorn at it?

Can you think of when we climbed the oak tree in your garden,
Then we fell twenty feet through the air and when your mum asked if we were okay we couldn't stop laughing.
Even though you broke your collar bone...........

I signed the cast with a smiley face because I knew that you would know it was me.

After all this time do you remember when we drifted apart?

You started to like football so you joined the school team and we got time apart.

I started to like school and read books while you were popular and played sports along with everyone else.

Then they started to tease me and you joined in. I stay indoors now.

We used to run through the trees and shout together, but these memories fade.

Why is it that these memories are dust – while I remember the memories, I want to forget.

Miles Edwards (age 11)

About Racism

No matter what the colour of our skin is
we all have something in common.
The colour of our skin makes people
angry and spit on us.
If someone calls us names they want us to be angry.
Hasim thinks it would be nice if people
Said he was their good friend.
Do they think we are animals because we
are black or even white?
Gengis comes from Turkey, he is white.
People call him names.
They say things like "Turkish delight" and
"I want you for my Christmas dinner".
There is writing on the walls by the
others about people coming from
different countries,
and they way they talk
and the colour of their skins
and the food they eat.
When we first see it, first,
we feel like writing things about them too
but if we don't it's because we don't know
who wrote those things.
They may be Bengali or English or anything.

If there was writing on the school
about Jamaicans,
we could ask our teacher or the school keeper
to try and get it off
because if a Jamaican new boy or girl
came to our school,
they would think we didn't like them,
and not want to come to our school.
Some of us think we should have more police.
They could stop the killings in the street.
But some of us think we have enough police
And that they can't be there at the right time anyway.
We wish we could share our luck
because we have friends and we can play
and not feel sad.
We aren't all friends yet
but we hope we are coming to be friends.

Gengis, Rahela, Tony, Jubez, Haqim, Zowrul,
Aklas, Aktar, David, Mark, Denise, Denise,
Azizun, Kahan, Kabiz and Ayesha (age 10)

Because We Care

Report it to sort it
And we will support it.
Report it to sort it and we will be there.

Everyone needs support and T.L.C.,
The thug the mug and people like me.
The helpless the lonely all need a friend.
To chillax and max with days on end.
No faker's takers or heart breakers.
Peace and love will always mate us.
War and crime will only break us.
But real friendship will forever make us.

Report it to sort it,
And we will support it.
Report it to sort it and we will be there.

If you've been physically hurt sometime,
Or put in a distressed state of mind.
If you're pushed and you've been shoved
And days have felt like there is no love
Life feels drab washing down a drain
As no one seems to see your pain,

Put these words on your brain
And repeat them over again and again.

Report it to sort it
And we will support it.
Report it to sort it and we will be there.

B to the U to the L.L.Y.,
It's time to give someone a blye.
Which simply means don't make them cry.
And why not try just to be nice,
It's the only way to be cool as ice.
No means once, it don't mean twice.

And everyone knows you could be great,
But it's always the victims left in a state.

Report it to sort it and we will support it.
Report it to sort it and we will be there.
Report it to sort it because we care.

Donavan Christopher

The Dare

Go on, I dare you,
come on down!

Was it *me* they called?
Pretend you haven't heard,
a voice commanded in my mind.
Walk past, walk fast
and don't look down,
don't look behind.

Come on, it's easy!

The banks were steep,
the water low
and flanked with oozing brown.
Easy? Walk fast
but don't look down.
Walk straight, walk on,
even risk their jeers
and run...

Never go near those dykes,
 my mother said.
No need to tell me.

I'd seen stones sucked in
and covered without trace,
gulls slide to bobbing safety,
grasses drown as water rose.
No need to tell me
to avoid the place.

She ca-a-a-n't, she ca-a-a-n't!
Cowardy, cowardy custard!

There's no such word as 'can't',
my father said.
I slowed my pace.
The voices stopped,
waited as I wavered, grasping breath.
My mother's wrath? My father's scorn?
A watery death?

I hesitated then turned back,
forced myself to see the mud below.
After all, it was a dare...
There was no choice;
I had to go.   *Judith Nicholls*

A Friend Like Me

I have trouble sharing –
Here, take my dirty sock,
While I just ride your scooter
All up and down the block.

And then I'll play your banjo,
Your rhinestone-studded drum,
And your can share my cookie,
At least this little crumb.

I'll share the wrappers from my
Three yummy candy bars,
Then I'll play with your spacemen
From Jupiter and Mars.

I have no trouble sharing
My teenie pencil stub,
While I take all your bath toys
To play with in the tub.

My momma says I've trouble
With sharing – it's not true –
I'll eat up all your cupcakes –
Here, hold my worn-out shoe.

I think a friend like me is
So very, very rare.
A kid that has no trouble
With knowing how to share.

Robert Scotellaro

"The friend is the man
who knows all about you,
and still likes you."
Elbert Hubbard

"Your Pick"

We line up.
"Your pick" says Skinner.
There's nothing worse than
 Being the last one picked.
We stand there
Waiting, making ourselves tall,
Saying nothing
But in our heads we're screaming
"Pick me! Pick me!"
Skinner looks along the line
Taking his time, drinking it in
"Your pick" he says again to Badger.
And Badger picks Wilson.
Another three and that's the school team gone.
Next it's the tallest
The biggest
The widest
"He'll do – he can go in defence"
And then Sharron Glass
With her sharp elbows
And then...

Then there's only two of us left
Standing, fidgeting with our hands
The others turning away, impatient now
Wanting to start the game.
It's over for them,
But not for us.
"Bates" says Badger.
And I feel myself become smaller.
I step forward
But Skinner pins me back with a stare
And then I see what's going to happen next.
And in that moment I know that
There is something worse –
Worse than being last one picked.
And as he turns away
He plunges the knife in.
"You can 'ave 'im" he says.

Ian MacDonald

Dream Team

My team
Will have all the people in it
Who're normally picked last.

Such as me.

When it's my turn to be chooser
I'll overlook Nick Magic-Feet-Jones
And Supersonic Simon Hughes

And I'll point at my best friend Sean
Who'll faint with surprise
And delight.

And at Robin who's always the one
Left at the end that no one chose –
Unless he's away, in which case it's guess who?

And Tim who can't see a thing
Without his glasses.
I'll pick him.

And the rest of the guys that Mr. Miller
Calls dead-legs but only need their chance
To show what they're made of.

We'll play in the cup final
In front of the class, the school, the town,
The world, the galaxy.

And due to the masterly leadership shown
By their captain, not forgetting
His three out-of-this-world goals,

We'll WIN.

Frances Nagle

Playgrounds

Playgrounds are such gobby places.
Know what I mean?
Everyone seems to have something to
Talk about, giggle, whisper, scream and shout
  about.
I mean, it's like being in a parrot cage.

And playgrounds are such pushy places.
Know what I mean?
Everyone seems to
Run about, jump, kick, do cartwheels, handstands,
  fly around,
I mean, it's like being inside a whirlwind.

And playgrounds are such patchy places
Know what I mean?
Everyone seems to
Go round in circles, lines and triangles, coloured
  shapes,
I mean, it's like being in a kaleidoscope.

And playgrounds are such pally places
Know what I mean?
Everyone seems to
Have best friends, secrets, link arms, be
  in gangs.
Everyone, except me.

Know what I mean?

Berlie Doherty

"Wishing to be friends is quick,
but friendship is a slow-ripening fruit."
Aristotle

Unlinked Arms

Splitting up with my best friend
was like shedding peas
from a pod
and popping them in
boiling water for a few minutes
It left me
with a soft wrinkled outer-coat
and hard inside.

Walking down
the broken hopscotch path
I reach the brook
where she had
mischievously thrown
the missing textbook
The delicious lie
we told the next day
mingles with the fogged
air of the past.

Splitting up with my best friend
I recall unshed tears
a Mona Lisa smile
and the brook
which carried my secrets
downstream
on rainy days.

What I remember most
are the unlinked arms
the unfollowed footsteps
And the solitary eating
of tuppenny liquorice.

Georgina Blake

Coventry

"Send her to Coventry" they said
"And if you talk to her you're dead.
If she even looks your way
Turn around and make her pay.

If she asks you what she's done
Walk off slowly (never run),
If she calls out after you
Let her, till her face turns blue.

If she takes you by surprise
Blank her out with stony eyes,
If her tears begin to flow
Make sure that she knows you know.

If she finds you after school
Don't go soft and break the rule,
If she sees you, try to hide
Or pass by on the other side."

So that is how it was, and then
Things became normal once again
But she'll recall for evermore
The town where no one talked to her.

John Mole

Someone 'sent to Coventry' is shunned, not spoken to, left out of everything and treated as if he or she is simply not there. Coventry is an English city, and the expression has an interesting history that is worth looking up.

"Never forget the days I spent with you. Continue to be my friend, as you will always find me yours."
Ludwig Van Beethoven

Many Ways

There are so many ways to say: "I'm sorry."

The polite way:
"My mistake. Forgive me."
The shy way:
"Whoops."
The puzzled way:
"I can't believe I did that."
The agonised way:
"My entire soul is tortured with shame."
The timid way:
"Please don't be angry with me."
The defensive way:
"It was an accident."
The courageous way:
"It was all my own fault."
The modest way:
"I am such a fool."
The sincere way:
"I shall never, ever do that again."

Little children sing it
When they trample mud across new rugs.
Old ladies giggle it
When they forget your name.
Shop girls recite it
When they run out of change.
Tall men mumble it
When they trample on your toes.
Even silent people signal it
With wide and sorrowful eyes.
Anyone can whisper it.

So why can't you ?

Clare Bevan

Copycats

I like her, I like her not.
We're best of friends, I hate her.
I'm turned to ice or furnace-hot
By my annoying imitator.

We laugh and whisper secrets,
But then she makes me mad,
When everything I choose or buy
She gets. (Or else she's had.)

"You know that dress you bought last week,
You'd been saving for so long?
I told my Dad how nice you looked –
Guess what? Now I've got one!"

It's dresses, CDs, songs and crisps,
It's everything that makes *me*.
When I turn to look at her
My reflection's what I see.

Do you know anyone like her?
Does your friend do it too?
If you have found the cure for this,
Please, may I copy you?

Daphne Kitching

Friends For Ever?

I really hope we never fall out
Or I grow to loathe the sight of your face,
As I've just written – in marker pen –
Your name on my pencil case.

Though, happily, I've just realised –
And, quite honestly, this really is great –
That there's still a space just above your name
Where I could always add 'I hate...'

Mike Barfield

"Good friends are like stars...
You don't always see them,
but you know they are always there."
Anonymous

Best Of Friends

Childhood Friend

She was always there for me
and rarely failed to see
my point of view in everything;
we'd never disagree.

In all our years together,
come rain or come shine,
as we talked and listened,
her wisdom echoed mine.

If actions needed justifying
she would always say
I'd done the right and proper thing;
her loyalty never swayed.

So deep a friendship as we had
you'd think would never end,
yet it couldn't last for ever
as I could not pretend
to keep as my companion
an Imaginary Friend.

Celia Warren

The Smile

It began with a whisper
But grew and grew
Until I felt certain
The source must be you.
Why did you smile
While I listened and then
Turn away as their faces
Fell silent again?

What had you told them
That slammed shut their looks
Like the end of a lesson
With unpopular books?
What was the writing
Which I couldn't see
As it hid between covers
And pointed at me?

Nothing much could have happened
For by the next day
We were laughing, talking,
And managed to stay
(Well, after a fashion)
Good friends for a while
But with always between us
The ghost of that smile.

John Mole

Left Out Together

There's the crowd of them again,
So happy and carefree,
Laughing and chatting and going somewhere –
Not including me.
They never say, "Why don't you come too?"
I wander away and pretend I don't care –
But I do.
And when they come back
They've got it all to remember
And share.
I wouldn't know:
I wasn't there.

You look as though
You might be feeling the same:
Left on the sidelines,
Out of the game .. ?
You are?
I was actually wondering whether
We could team up and both be
Left out together.

Eric Finney

Difference Of Opinion

My Mum doesn't like Paul.
Whenever he comes round to call
She keeps him waiting in the hall.
She doesn't do that to my other friends at all.

Mum says he's rude and cheeky.
She says he's sly and sneaky.
I think his sense of humour's freaky.
He's really cool. He is not geeky.

Grown ups don't like Paul – it's true
And the reasons they don't like him
Are the reasons why I do.

Jan Dean

"Good friends are hard to find,
harder to leave, and impossible
to forget."
Anonymous

The Friendship Bench

Every colour
   and every creed,
People with money
   and people in need.
We want
everyone sitting on the friendship bench.

Football fans
   from rival teams.
"Beat you next time."
   "In your dreams."

We want mums and dads
   who can't get along,
brothers and sisters
   always in the wrong.
We want
everyone sitting on the friendship bench.

We want families crying,
   squabbling, bickering,
noisy neighbours
   tempers quickening.

Overloud voices
  sounding out,
pressure groups shouting
  what they're about,
everyone sitting on the friendship bench.

We want criminals, judges,
  prisoners and jailers,
bullies and victims,
  thieves, blackmailers,
everyone sitting on the friendship bench.

No need to argue,
  no need to fight,
nobody thinking that
  might is right,
just
everyone sitting on the friendship bench.

We want positive, negative,
  black and white,
we want darkness giving way
  to the light.

We want hope for the future,
    lessons from the past,
the sort of friendship
    that lasts and lasts,
we want
everyone sitting on the friendship bench.

We want aggravation,
    assimilation,
recrimination,
    United Nations,
everyone sitting on the friendship bench.

From the naughty corner
    to the friendship bench,

everyone sitting on the friendship bench,
everyone sitting on the friendship bench,
everyone sitting on the friendship bench.

So go on, say who
   you'd like to see,
on the friendship bench
   sitting peacefully
with you
and
me.

   Brian Moses

Please feel free to use this poem in assemblies, to adapt it,
write extra verses, take verses away, add shakers to
underpin the rhythm, etc. When I first wrote this poem it
was nine pages long! This is the condensed version! BM

"The best kind of friend is one with whom you
can sit on a bench saying nothing and when you
get up and go, you feel you have had the best
conversation of your life."

Anonymous

A Best Friend Is . . .

Someone who laughs at the same things
who lifts you up when you're down
and when you're way too high
helps keep your feet
on the ground.

Someone who'll share homework
help you revise for tests (or maybe not!)
and when you both get C's
blows a raspberry, says
"So what?"

Someone you trust with your iPod
who'll lend you her best top because
you've got NOTHING ELSE
which will go (even though
she wants to wear it herself).

Someone who goes fair shares
when you're out with the crowd
but would split her last
choc bar or smoothie
if you were stony broke.

Someone who listens, swops stories
for hours on end, and you never
have to bite your tongue
or choose your words
but can just be yourself.

Someone to tell your dreams to –
who dreams with you when you say
"I'll be a catwalk queen, marry
Prince Harry, win 'X Factor',
be the first woman on Mars."

Someone who says nothing
when you're sad, just lets you
wrap your arms around her
stays the whole distance
never lets you down.

(Oh, yes, and has the same taste in boys
but never goes after yours).

   Patricia Leighton

The Injection

I lined up near the door
Just behind Maggy Moore.
We'd rolled up our sleeves,
And I could see her arm,
All freckly like Steve's,
And rather thin. *No harm
In asking*, I thought.
So I said, "Are you scared?"
"A bit," she said. "Are you?"
"No," I said. But I'd been taught not to lie, so I said,
"Well, that's not really true.
I am a bit, too."

I stood with my arm bared,
And thoughts whizzing round in my head.
One at a time we went in.
"Last of this batch,"
Said the nurse. She rubbed my skin
With something cold. Then, like a pin,
A little sharp scratch.

It didn't really hurt, not much.
Rolling down my sleeve
I went back to our class.
And I was going to sit by Steve,
But there was Maggy in her place
And to my great surprise
She had tears in her eyes.
"It wasn't as bad as that,"
I said. She burst out crying.
Crying! At her table. In Year Four!

I gave her a gum and sat by her.
Her face was on fire.
"It wasn't really bad," she said.
"I was just frightened." And Miss Lyon
Came over. "Oh I'll leave her with you.
You're doing so well." So I sat
By Maggy and we had a chat,
Not much – about this and that.
And that day a silence was broken,
Because I'd never ever spoken
    To Maggy before.

Gerard Benson

Friendship

Friendship
Is precious
Keep it
Protect it
You will need it
Don't throw it away
Don't break it
Don't neglect it
Keep it
Somewhere
In your heart
If you want to
Somewhere in your thoughts
If you want to
But keep it
For, friendship
Has no borders

And its boundary
Is that of the world
It is the colour
Of the rainbow
And it has the beauty
Of a dream
Never listen
To those who say
It doesn't exist any more
It is here
It is yours
When you want it
All you have to do is:
Open
Your eyes

Véronique Tadjo

Mutual Wish

If only I was Natalie,
I'd have everything going for me.
She's a brilliant friend and we gossip no end,
but I just wish *she* was *me*.

She's quick, sly, slick, knows every trick,
makes things happen, makes life tick;

she's a joker, a mimic, a rebel, a cynic –
looks on life as one big gimmick.

She's wild and daring past all caring –
there's simply no comparing her
with cautious, mousy me.

But guess what Natalie said to me
yesterday in the dinner queue – suddenly, right out of the blue!
She said: "I wish I was you."

Kate Williams

Sometimes!

Sometimes he's a red Porsche 911,
Sometimes he's a fruit and nutcase from outer space,
Sometimes he's the lie that you wish was the truth
And sometimes he's………the warmth inside a smile.

Sometimes he's the flip and jump in a seaside wave,
Sometimes he's a packet of crisps when you have toothache,
Sometimes he's the itch in the sand between your toes
And sometimes he's the twinkle in the black of a night sky.

Sometimes he's the exclamation mark in a sentence,
Sometimes he's a heavyweight boxing glove,
Sometimes he's a bag of multi-coloured crayons
And sometimes, and best of all, he's… simply my best friend!

Ian Souter

Everything's Better With You

jokes are much funnier
holidays sunnier
everything's better with you

biscuits are crunchier
popcorn is munchier
bananas are bunchier
everything's better with you

homework is easier
life's bright and breezier
pizza is cheesier
ice cream is freezier
everything's better with you

sherbet is fizzier
buzzing bees busier
fairground rides dizzier
questions are quizzier
frisbees are whizzier
everything's better with you

colours are zingier
microwaves pingier
church bells are ringier
gold chains are blingier
and you're just hum-dingier
super song singier
everything's better with you
oh everything's better with you

Jan Dean

"In the sweetness of friendship
let there be laughter,
and sharing of pleasures."
Kahil Gaibran

Oath Of Friendship

SHANG YA!
I want to be your friend
For ever and ever without break or decay.
When the hills are flat
And the rivers are all dry,
When it lightens and thunders in winter,
When it rains and snows in summer,
When Heaven and Earth mingle –
Not till then will I part from you.

Author unknown (1st Century BC, China)
Translated by Arthur Waley

"Remember, the greatest gift
is not found in a store nor under a tree,
but in the hearts of true friends."
Cindy Lew

Final Words...

*When you meet your friend,
your face brightens –
you have struck gold.*

Kassia (9th Century BC, Greece)

*With clothes the new are best;
with friends the old are best.*

Traditional proverb, China

Beat Those Bullies

You don't have to let a bully make your life miserable. You don't have to live your life looking over your shoulder, peeping round street corners, frightened to turn on your computer or phone in case there is another vicious message. You don't have to live like that... but you do need help. You can't tackle this on your own.

If you are being bullied, tell an adult you can trust. Tell your parents, your older brother or sister, your teacher or headteacher. My mother used to say to me, "A trouble shared is a trouble halved" and it's true. With someone else sharing your worry it won't seem so bad.

You can also find helpful advice on the Internet and these websites are a good place to start:

If you're being bullied, ChildLine can help you to make it stop now:
http://www.childline.org.uk/Bullying

Face bullying with confidence and learn how
to stay safe:
   http://www.kidpower.org

Information for young people, parents and teachers
on tackling bullying within schools:
   http://www.antibullying.net

Bullying advice, anti-bullying resources for schools
and tips on how to prevent bullying:
   http://www.kidscape.org.uk/

Don't let a bully control your life.

Beat that bully.

   Brian Moses

Acknowledgements

All copyright poems reproduced by kind permission of the authors, including these poems previously published:

Robert Scotellaro for *A Friend Like Me* © Robert Scotellaro, previously published in *Snail Stampede and Other Poems* by Robert Scotellaro (Hands Up Books, 2004), John Foster for *And How Was School Today?* © John Foster, previously published in *The Poetry Chest* by John Foster (Oxford University Press, 2007), Mick Gowar for *Barry* © Mick Gowar, Daphne Kitching for *Copycats* © Daphne Kitching, previously published in *I'm in a Mood Today: Poems about Feelings* by John Foster (Oxford University Press, 2000), John Mole for *Coventry* © John Mole, previously published in *The Dummy's Dilemma and Other Poems* by John Mole (Hodder Children's Books, 1999), John Mole for *The Smile* © John Mole, previously published in *Boo to a Goose* by John Mole (Peterloo Poets, 1987), Judith Nicholls for *The Dare* © Judith Nicholls, previously published in *Midnight Forest* by Judith Nicholls (Faber and Faber, 1987), David Harmer for *Dobbo's First Swimming Lesson* © David Harmer, previously published in *The Very Best of David Harmer* (Macmillan Children's Books, 2001), Frances Nagle for *Dream Team* © Frances Nagle, previously published in *Read Me 2: Poems for every day of the year* (Macmillan Children's Books, 1999), *The Works 2: Poems for every subject and for every occasion* (Macmillan Children's Books, 2002) and *You Can't Call a Hedgehog Hopscotch: Poems for Children* by Frances Nagle (Dagger Press, 1999), Fred Sedgwick for *The Fight* © Fred Sedgwick, previously published in *Here Comes the Poetry Man* (Salt Publishing, 2011), Gerard Benson for *The Injection* © Gerard Benson, previously published in *To Catch an Elephant* by Gerard Benson (Smith/Doorstep Books, 2002), Bernard Young for *I Wish I was a Robot* © Bernard Young, previously published in *Brilliant! 50 Dazzling Poems* by Bernard Young (Kingston Press, 2000), Brian Moses for *The Bully* © Brian Moses, previously published in *The Great Galactic Ghoul* by Brian Moses (Caboodle Books, 2009), The poets of *About Racism* © Gengis, Rahela, Tony, Jubez, Haqim, Zowrul, Aklas, Aktar, David, Mark, Denise, Denise, Azizun, Kahan, Kabiz & Ayesha, previously published in *Free My Mind – An anthology of Black and Asian Poetry* – Edited by Judith Elkin & Carlton Duncan (Hamish Hamilton Ltd, 1990), Georgina Blake for *Unlinked Arms* © Georgina Blake, previously published in *Free My Mind – An anthology of Black and Asian Poetry* – Edited by Judith Elkin & Carlton Duncan (Hamish Hamilton Ltd, 1990), Véronique Tadjo for *Friendship* © Véronique Tadjo, previously published in *Talking Drums – a Selection of Poems from Africa South of the Sahara* by Véronique Tadjo (A & C Black, 2001), Berlie Doherty for *Playgrounds* © Berlie Doherty, previously published in *Walking on Air* (Hodder Children's Books, 1999), Gareth Owen for *New Boy* © Gareth Owen, previously published in *Collected Poems for Children* by Gareth Owen (Macmillan Children's Books, 2001), obtainable from the poet's website http://garethowen.com and Kate Williams for *Mutual Wish* © Kate Williams, previously published in *My Gang* by Brian Moses (Macmillan Children's Books, 1999).